My CORNish Holiday

Written and illustrated by Alix Wood

choughins

Choughins is an imprint of Tor Mark
www.tormark.co.uk

Published by Tor Mark,
United Downs Industrial Estate,
St Day, Redruth, Cornwall TR16 5HY

Published 2010, reprinted 2011
This reprint 2019

ISBN 978 0 85025 101 2

Printed and bound in Great Britain by
St Austell Printing Company.

About me

Name

Age

Home town

Hobbies

Favourite food

Favourite colour

Favourite animal

Favourite TV programme

Best friend

Why not keep a holiday diary on the special pages in this book. It will remind you of all the things you did and be a fun souvenir.

My Holiday Diary

My holiday family

Who is on holiday with you? Draw them here. You could draw your pets, or even your favourite toys, too.

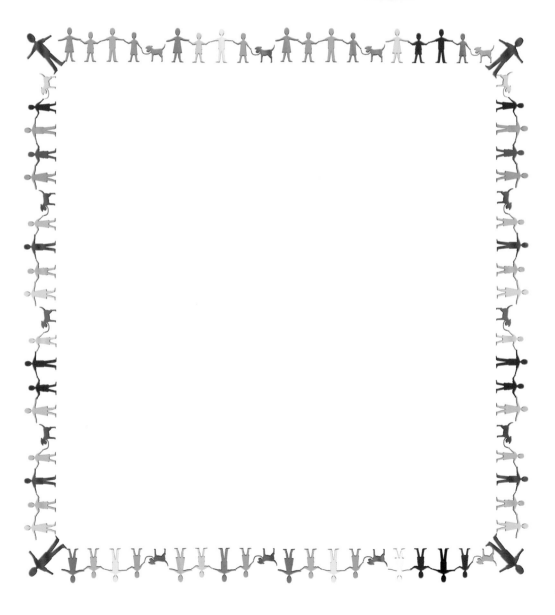

On holiday with me is...

Did you make any friends on holiday?

My friends' names were

My contacts

Have you contacted anyone
while you were away? How?

Name of friend or relation	Phoned them?	Texted them?	Sent a postcard?	Other

You can write some useful numbers and addresses
here

My plans

Things I'd like to see and do on holiday

My map of Cornwall

Here is a map of Cornwall with some of the big roads and towns on. Do you know where you went on your holiday? You can mark them on the map or make a list of places here.

Boscastle

Tintagel

Camelford

Port Isaac

Polzeath

Rock

A39

Padstow

Wadebridge

Porth

St Columb Major

Bodmin

Lanivet

A3

Newquay

Lostwithie

Roche

Par

St Dennis

Perranporth

Fowey

St Stephen

St Austell

St Agnes

A30

Mevagissey

Portreath

Truro

Gwithian

Redruth

A39

Gorran Haven

St Ives

Veryan

Feock

Hayle

Zennor

Camborne

Penryn

Madron

Stithians

St Mawes

St Just

Breage

A394

Mawnan

Falmouth

Penzance

Newlyn

Helston

Helford

Land's End

Porthleven

St Keverne

Porthcurno

Mullion

Lizard

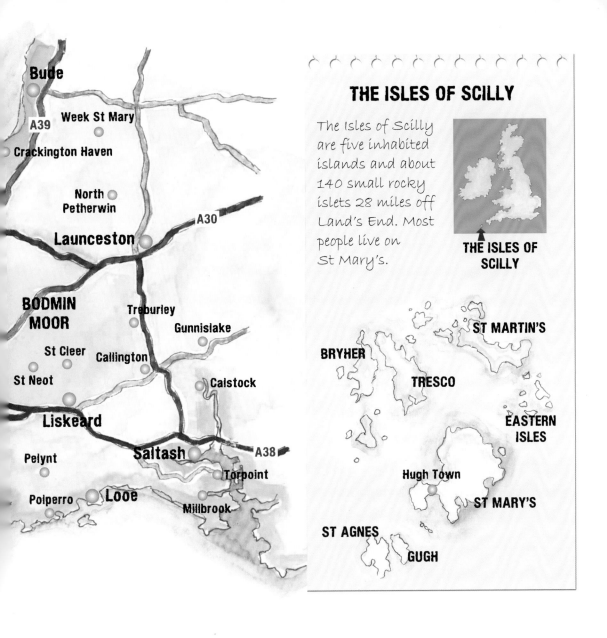

THE ISLES OF SCILLY

The Isles of Scilly are five inhabited islands and about 140 small rocky islets 28 miles off Land's End. Most people live on St Mary's.

THE ISLES OF SCILLY

ST MARTIN'S

BRYHER

TRESCO

EASTERN ISLES

Hugh Town

ST MARY'S

ST AGNES

GUGH

Bude

A39

Week St Mary

Crackington Haven

North Petherwin

A30

Launceston

BODMIN MOOR

Treburley

Gunnislake

St Cleer

Callington

St Neot

Calstock

Liskeard

Saltash

A38

Pelynt

Torpoint

Polperro

Looe

Millbrook

What was your...	from	to
longest journey?		
prettiest journey?		
most boring journey?		
wiggliest journey?		
scariest journey?		

My holiday home

Are you in a tent?
Or a caravan?
Or a house?
Or a hotel?

Draw your holiday home here.

Room checklist

- [ ] bed
- [ ] wardrobe
- [ ] chest of drawers
- [ ] chair
- [ ] carpet
- [ ] mirror
- [ ] sink
- [ ] picture
- [ ] window

What else does
your room have?

My Holiday Diary

My suitcase

What did you bring with you? Pack this suitcase full of drawings of your belongings.

Did you need everything?

Are there some things you should
have left at home?

....

....

Are there some things you forgot?

....

....

....

....

....

....

....

....

My journey

What transport have you used on your holiday?

Give a tick if you have EVER been in any of these.

- [ ] train
- [ ] car
- [ ] motorhome
- [ ] boat
- [ ] plane
- [ ] helicopter
- [ ] jetski
- [ ] ferry
- [ ] bus
- [ ] cable car
- [ ] coach

- [ ] horse
- [ ] tractor
- [ ] quadbike
- [ ] motorbike
- [ ] bicycle
- [ ] skateboard
- [ ] traction engine
- [ ] surfboard
- [ ] rollerblades
- [ ] trike
- [ ] scooter

Car badge bingo

Give a tick for each badge when you see them

My best meal

Draw your favourite meal that you had on holiday on this Cornishware plate.

Food checklist
Tick the foods you like ✓

- ☐ apples
- ☐ sausages
- ☐ biscuits
- ☐ fish
- ☐ bananas
- ☐ raisins
- ☐ eggs

- ☐ bacon
- ☐ cheese
- ☐ toast
- ☐ cereal
- ☐ carrots
- ☐ chicken
- ☐ cake

My worst meal

Draw your WORST meal here

Cornwall spotter game

Here is a list of things you might see on your holiday. You get a point for each one you see. Look out for the bonus points too!

- [ ] Cornish flag
- [ ] Sheep
- [ ] Buzzard **BONUS 10 POINTS**
- [ ] Clotted cream
- [ ] Ice cream van
- [ ] Pasty
- [ ] The sea
- [ ] Chough **BONUS 40 POINTS**
- [ ] Caravan
- [ ] Seal **BONUS 30 POINTS**

- [ ] Tin Mine
- [ ] Seaweed
- [ ] Wild pony **BONUS 10 POINTS**
- [ ] Gorse bush
- [ ] Castle
- [ ] Beast of Bodmin **BONUS 50 POINTS**
- [ ] Fishing boat
- [ ] Surfer
- [ ] Tractor
- [ ] Rainbow **BONUS 20 POINTS**

TOTAL 180

1-14 = good   15-35 = well done   36-96 = fantastic
97-120 = wow!   121-180 = amazing!

My Holiday Diary

My scrapbook page

Here is some space for doodles, writing, lists and other stuff that will remind you of your holiday. Maybe list King Arthur's knights, or draw the animals you have seen?

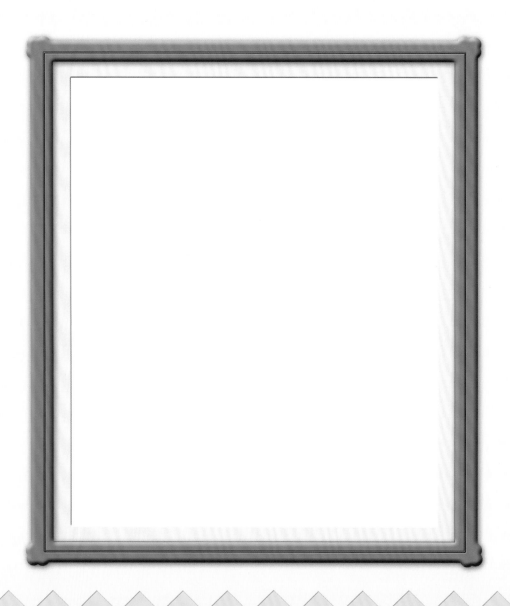

Stick any tickets and souvenirs on this page

Draw your own postcard

Greetings from Cornwall

My weather chart

Here is a chart where you can record the weather for your holiday. Write or draw the weather in the squares. Which was the best day?

Holiday weather

Day 1	Day 2	Day 3	Day 4	Day 5	Day 6	Day 7

Day 8	Day 9	Day 10	Day 11	Day 12	Day 13	Day 14

Order your favourite weather from 1-10, 1 for the best, and 10 for worst

☐	sun		☐	warm
☐	rain		☐	hot
☐	wind		☐	hail
☐	snow		☐	thunder
☐	cold		☐	clouds

My holiday centre

Where are you staying on your holiday?

- [ ] Village
- [ ] City
- [ ] Holiday Park
- [ ] Town
- [ ] Countryside

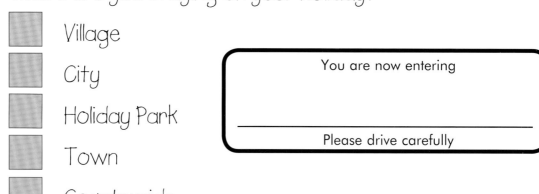

You are now entering

_____

Please drive carefully

Write a poem about it

There was an old man from St Blazey
Who could be incredibly lazy
While picking wild flowers
It took him three hours
To gather just one measly daisy.

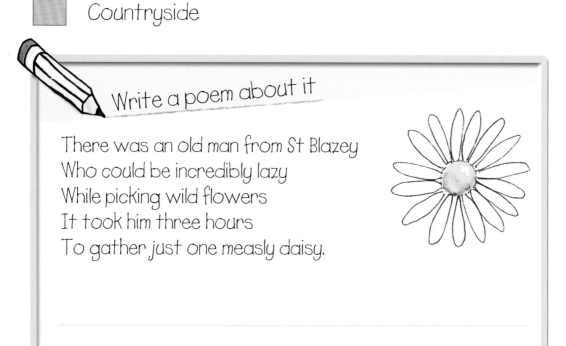

Draw the best flower or the loveliest pebble you found here.

My Photo album

If you take any photos,
you can stick some here.

My Holiday Diary

Questionnaire

What was the scariest thing you did?

What did you do for the first time?

What was the funniest thing?

What was the most boring thing?

Who was the grumpiest?

What did you do that you were proudest of?

Which animals did you make friends with?

What did you learn on your holiday?

What did you see that you'd never seen before?

What would you do again if you could?

What did you buy or find that will remind you of your holiday?

CORNWALL

Best Place Certificate

This is to certify that

....

was the best place I went to on holiday.

Signed

....

(Cornwall Holiday Expert)

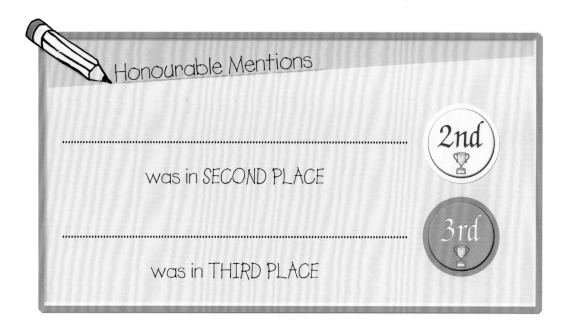

Honourable Mentions

.... **2nd**

was in SECOND PLACE

.... **3rd**

was in THIRD PLACE

and in
last place...

The
**Worst Place
on my Holiday
Prize**
goes to

_____
_____

Why?

What did other
people think?

Holiday review

Give each category a mark out of ten.
Then add them all up to get your Holiday Score

___/10 Companions

___/10 Accommodation

___/10 Fun

___/10 Transport

___/10 Food

___/10 Friendly people

___/10 Weather

___/10 Scenery

___/10 Adventures

___/10 Things to do

My Cornish Holiday
Score is

100

0-40
Better luck
next time!

41-70
Good Holiday

71-100
Top Holiday